Understanding and Using the Light Microscope

Introduction and QuickStart Guide to Using Compound Light Microscopes

GW00537594

Dr Chris Thomas & Lewis Woolnough

Copyright 2014 Dr Chris Thomas & Lewis Woolnough
First published in 2014 by
Milton Contact Ltd
3rd Reprint 2017

A CIP catalogue record for this book is available from
The British Library

ISBN: 978-0-9929289-2-6

Printed in United Kingdom

Milton Contact Ltd
3 Hall End, Milton, Cambridge, UK
CB24 6AQ

www.miltoncontact.co.uk

Contents

Figure 1. Cross section through a sea-urchin spine (photo negative) 100x.

Aim:

This booklet begins with a "Quickstart" section for those eager to start using their microscope immediately. You are then given more information on the parts of the microscope, how to set it up and use it.

This is the first of a series of booklets that aims to give you an enjoyable, practical and informative guide to using and understanding the microscope.

Videos

There are nine videos accompanying this book. Look out for the link information in red. There is also a QR Code for each video, like the one here, below on the right. If you have a smart phone or a tablet, you can download a bar scanner app that will read the QR Code and take you to the online video.

Video "The parts of the microscope"
http://goo.gl/tre3AQ

The Microscopy Series

As with anything, you will get far more out of your microscope if you understand what it does and how it works. Further booklets in the series will cover subjects including:

- Photography through the microscope;
- Light & contrast methods for the compound microscope;
- Lenses, images and resolution in the compound microscope.

Figure 2. Tip of worker honey bee sting 400x.

Introduction

This series looks at the COMPOUND MICROSCOPE, used when you wish to get a clear view of fine detail in a subject or see very small objects such as cells or bacteria. The range of magnification extends from about 30x to 1000x. The smallest objects you can see clearly are the size of bacteria, at around 1/1000 of a millimetre.

There are usually three different reasons for your needing to understand and use a microscope:

- Your job requires you to use one;
- You want to explore micro-worlds for fun;
- Your education/training requires it.

Fortunately, more than one can apply.

Studying subjects at a microscopic level has a tremendous range of applications in widely different fields: From metallurgy and medicine to marine life; pollen studies to pollutants; forensics to fine arts; chemistry to cooking, to name but a few.

Understanding and using a microscope properly can give you a great deal of pleasure as well as the satisfaction of using this tool professionally.

As a modern-day user, you join a long list of illustrious scientists, technicians and amateurs – from Robert Hooke in the 17th century to modern researchers at the cutting edge of science today.

The instrument itself is the iconic symbol for science. By the beginning of the 20th century, optics were already very advanced. Whilst there have been improvements and specialisations since, the basic principles of the compound microscope remain the same.

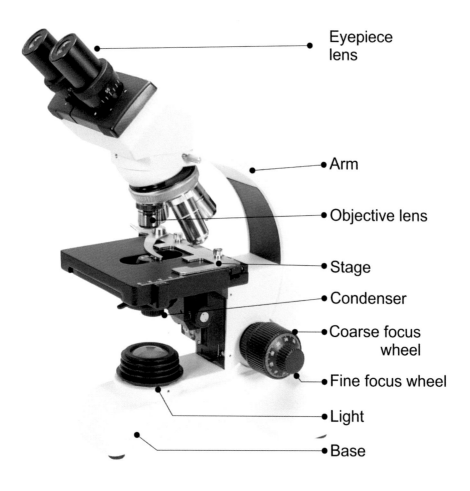

Eyepiece lens

Arm

Objective lens

Stage

Condenser

Coarse focus wheel

Fine focus wheel

Light

Base

Figure 3. Example of a compound microscope showing the key parts (photo Brunel Microscopes).

Quickstart Guide

This section gives you basic information and procedures that let you get started with most compound microscopes. Later sections of this booklet give you supporting information on the parts of the microscope and on using it to its full potential.

If you have instructions for your microscope, it would be helpful to read them.

Warning! Always carry your microscope with one hand gripping a convenient sturdy part such as the arm (but not the stage) and the other beneath the base, giving support. Do not tip the instrument upside down because some of the lenses may fall out if you do this!

Find the following on your instrument using figure 3:

1. **Eyepiece lens.** There may be two of these if you have a binocular type.
2. **Objective lens(es).** These are closest to the specimen on the stage.
3. **The stage.** This is the platform, with a hole though the centre, on which the specimen is placed.
4. **The focusing wheel.** In most cases there will be a large wheel for coarse focusing and a smaller one for delicate adjustments.
5. **The condenser.** This focuses light onto the sample. Note: basic microscopes may not have one.
6. **Inbuilt light or mirror** (for use with external light).
7. **Base.** The stable foundation to support the rest of the microscope.

More information in
The Essential Parts of a Compound Microscope on page 11.

Quick Reference Sheet: Setting up your microscope

Figure 4. Quick Reference sheet.

Download a reference copy of p8-9 to print https://goo.gl/fu7dYr

©Chris Thomas, Milton Contact Ltd
From "Understanding and Using the Light Microscope" 2014.

Quick Reference Sheet: Setting up your microscope

1. Prepare sample on microscope slide.

2. Ensure microscope is on stable surface.

3. Adjust seating.

4. Turn on microscope lighting.

5. Select low power 10x objective. Ensure there will be adequate space between objective and sample.

6. Check view through eyepiece. You should see a circle of light.

7. Place microscope slide on stage.

8. Looking from the side, use the coarse focus wheel to place objective close to sample.

9. Look through the eyepiece. Gradually **increase** the distance between objective and the sample. The sample should come into focus. Use fine focus wheel if required.

10. Focus the lamp iris diaphragm onto the specimen using the condenser. Then open the diaphragm till just out of field of view.

11. Adjust the condenser iris diaphragm to the correct setting for the objective in use.

12. Higher magnification: **If using parfocal objectives,** go to next suitable higher magnification objective and focus using fine adjustment. Repeat steps 10 & 11. **Otherwise,** increase objective distance from sample, move next objective into position and follow steps 8 to 11.

13. When finished, turn off microscope light, set back to lowest power objective and protect microscope from dust until next use.

More detailed instructions and explanations can be found later in
Setting up your microscope with visible light, page 27

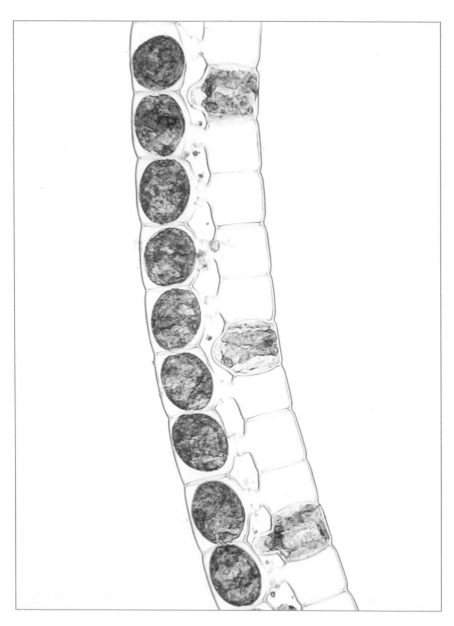

Figure 5. Spirogyra sp. spores 400x.

The Essential Parts of a Compound Microscope

Any microscope will work only if there is an appropriate supply of light. The light has to be directed onto or through a specimen, with which it interacts.

The microscope then collects and manipulates the light using lenses to form images that we can see.

Lenses are the parts that enable microscopes to make the images. A lens can be as simple as one specially-shaped piece of glass, but there are usually two or more glass elements mounted together in a short tube; the most complicated (and expensive) lenses have 15 or so glass elements.

Every compound microscope has two lenses. One, the objective lens, is positioned near to the object and makes a magnified primary image. The second lens is used to examine the primary image; it gives further magnification and modifies the image for the observer's eye to receive it. This is the eyepiece (or eye-lens).

A Basic Compound Microscope

The photograph on the next page (figure 6) shows a simple compound microscope. It has only the bare essentials for such an instrument.

See if you can identify the parts of the microscope using the text and the labels in figure 3.

Video "The parts of the microscope"
http://goo.gl/tre3AQ

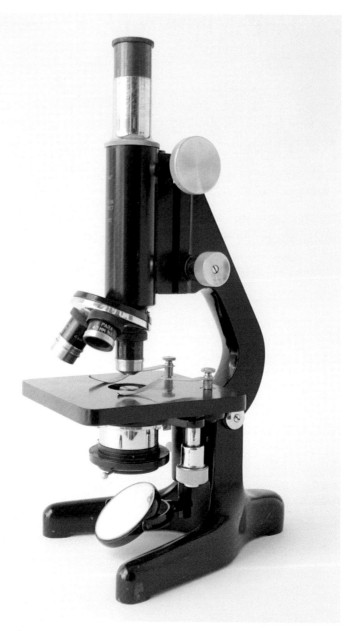

Figure 6. A basic compound microscope with a mirror (Watson).

The microscope's lenses are mounted in a tube, the eyepiece at the top and several objectives on a rotating mount at the lower end. The amount of detail to be seen and the magnification can be varied by changing either, or both, of the lenses.

The magnification of the microscope is **Eyepiece magnification x Objective magnification.** A 10x eyepiece and a 40x objective = 400x magnification.

The tube with the eyepiece and objectives is attached to the stand.

In figure 6, the tube can be moved away from, or closer to, the sample by means of two focusing wheels; the larger coarse focus which is used to position the tube to approximately the right height, and the smaller fine focus which is used for precision focusing.

The stage of the microscope is also attached to the stand.

The sample (usually mounted on a microscope slide) is placed over the hole in the stage and held in place, for example by using clips.

Below and attached to the stage is the condenser. This collects light and focuses it onto the sample on the stage via one or more lenses. The condenser shown has an iris diaphragm. The condenser iris diaphragm adjusts the cone of light entering the condenser.

A good condenser is essential for resolution.

Below the diaphragm, there is often a filter holder.

The base of the stand either contains a built-in lamp or a mirror with which to direct light into the microscope. In this case, it is a mirror.

Where a microscope has a lamp, it may also have an iris diaphragm (the lamp iris diaphragm) and a filter holder.

The whole system of light – (mirror) – condenser – sample – objective – eyepiece is aligned along a common axis, the so called optical axis of the microscope.

Variations on the basic structure

The compound microscope has evolved into a variety of forms, depending on manufacturer and use. The following variations may be found on your microscope, singly or in combination.

Eyepieces

A microscope may either have one eyepiece to look through (monocular), or two eyepieces to look through simultaneously, (binocular). On the binocular 'head', one or both of the eyepieces can be adjusted in focus to suit each eye. The distance between the eyepieces can be adjusted to suit individual users. Trinocular heads to allow camera attachment are also possible.

For optimum performance, the eyepieces on each microscope are specifically tailored to match the objectives.

Figure 7. A pair of eyepieces.

Video "Key Lenses of the Microscope"
http://goo.gl/v5EYub

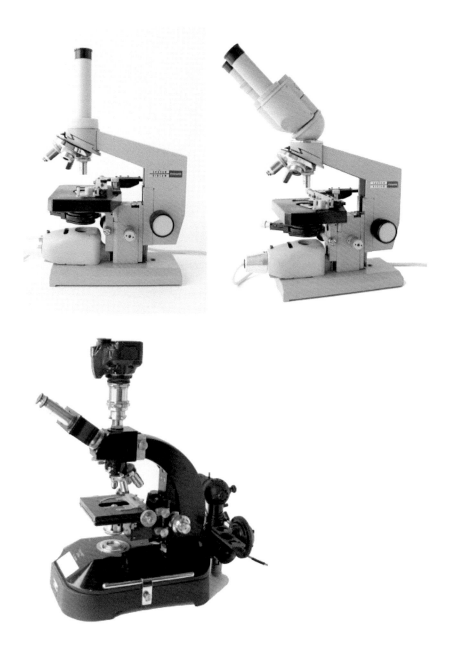

Figure 8. Microscopes with monocular, binocular & trinocular head.

Objectives

The objectives on a microscope are its key lenses. They differ in magnification and resolution. A microscope will generally have three or more objectives mounted on a rotating mount. Ideally the lenses are 'parfocal' – this means that when you change from a low power to a higher power objective, you only need to adjust the fine focus to sharpen the image.

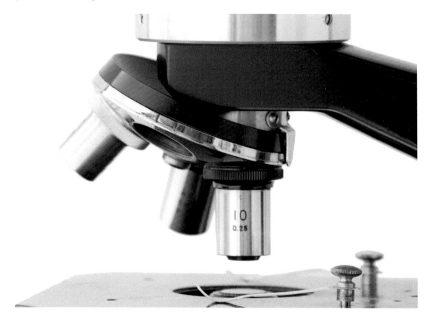

Figure 9. Objectives on a rotating mount.

Objectives come in a range of different magnifications and properties. Typical magnifications are 4x, 10x, 20x or 25x and 40x.

At higher magnifications, special lenses are used, e.g. oil immersion objectives, or in some instances, water immersion objectives. These are typically marked as OI (Oil immersion) or WI (Water immersion). For these objectives to work at their optimum optical resolution, they require an oil or water bridge between the sample and the objective. For the 100x oil immersion objective, you also need a suitable condenser. This also needs an oil bridge between the condenser and the sample (see p20, Condensers).

There are two types of objective system now in use: the traditional and the newer infinity lenses. Each system requires its own objectives and corresponding eyepieces. They are not interchangeable.

Standard lenses are called achromatic and are partially corrected for colour and distortion. Objectives with the highest levels of correction are labelled "apochromatic"; those with a full field of view in focus throughout are called "plan" or planar. There are also objectives for specific optical techniques such as phase contrast or interference microscopy.

Figure 10. A selection of objectives.

An objective is usually labelled with its magnification and numerical aperture (NA). The NA defines the amount of detail a lens can see – its resolution. A 4x objective with an NA of 0.1 can resolve points more than 2.75µm apart (micrometre, 1µm = 1/1000mm); a 10x objective, NA 0.25, can resolve points 1.1µm apart and a 40x objective, NA 0.65, can resolve points separated by 0.42µm.

Video "Key Lenses of the Microscope"
http://goo.gl/v5EYub

Focusing

Microscopes can also vary in how they focus on the sample. Either the tube holding the eyepiece and the objectives is moved to achieve focusing, as in figure 6, or the tube is static and it is the stage on which the sample sits that is moved up and down (figure 11).

Some microscopes have a scale for fine focus, so that the focus can be adjusted in precise steps through a sample (figure 11).

Figure 11. Top - Focus wheels that move stage up and down. Left –scale for fine focusing.

Video *"Focusing your Microscope"*
http://goo.gl/y6MUOz

The microscope stage

The stage or table of the microscope holds the sample. In the simplest instance, there are two spring clips to hold microscope slides in place (figure 12).

Many microscopes either have an integrated or attached mechanical stage, where the sample is held and can be moved mechanically and more accurately by turning precision knobs. The mechanical stages may also have Vernier scales that allow you to record the precise location of a particular feature on a slide.

There are also rotating stages – useful when using polarized light and filters.

Inverted microscopes have mechanical stages that will take petri-dishes or culture vessels for viewing live cultures (see p24).

Figure 12. Microscope stages. Top Left - simple clip to hold sample. Top Right - mechanical stage for precision movement. Left – Rotating stage.

Video "The Microscope stage"
http://goo.gl/YorNYr

Condensers

Most microscopes have a condenser below the stage as shown in figure 13. Condensers usually come with at least one iris diaphragm (aperture diaphragm) to help optimise illumination of the sample.

Condensers may also have filter holders, e.g. for neutral density filters to reduce the light intensity or for colour filters.

On some microscopes, the condensers can either have a flip top or interchangeable lens to give a wider illuminated area for microscopy with low power objectives of 4x magnification or less (see Part 3: Low magnification with 4x objectives or less).

For microscope viewing with high power 100x objectives, some condensers permit the use of oil as an optical bridge between condenser and slides for highest resolution (see Part 4: High magnification with objectives greater than 40x).

Condensers play an important role in achieving the optimum resolution of your sample. They collect the light from the microscope lamp and focus a cone of light onto the sample.

The cone of light produced by the condenser is adjusted to almost fill the current objective using the condenser's aperture diaphragm. The aperture is controlled either by a lever or knurled knob. This cone of light needs to be adjusted for each individual objective whenever you change magnification.

The condenser will have a numerical aperture (NA) value. For optimum resolution, the condenser NA should be equal to or greater than that of the objective being used.

Specialised optical systems, such as phase contrast or interference microscopes, have their own condensers.

If you do not have a condenser but do have a double sided mirror, use the concave side to focus the light on the specimen.

Figure 13. Top - flip top condenser with filter holder. bottom - Condenser in situ under stage of a microscope (Nikon).

Video "The Microscope Condenser"
http://goo.gl/701pFm

Lighting

Microscopes require light. External natural light can be used, for example a clear patch of blue sky reflected via a mirror into the microscope. **DANGER – DO NOT USE DIRECT SUNLIGHT.**

Artificial lighting gives a reliable standard source. This can either be a lamp external to the microscope or one built into it (figures 14 & 15).

Lights can range from simple bulbs to lamps with an iris diaphragm and the opportunity to add filters. The lamp iris diaphragm (field diaphragm) controls the circular area of the sample that is illuminated. The aim is to just fill the visible sample area for the objective and avoid extra stray light which could degrade the image.

The source and quality of light will be considered later in the series.

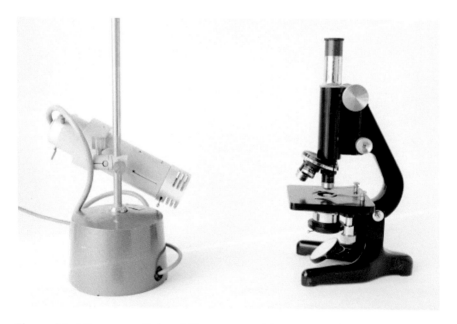

Figure 14. Microscope lights: Microscope with mirror and external lamp.

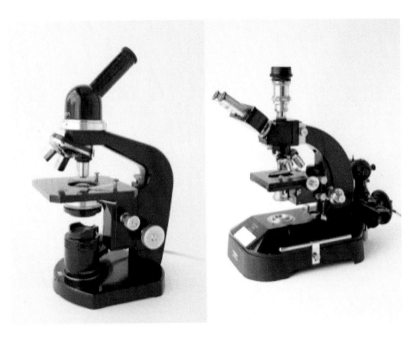

Figure 15. Microscope lights: left - base light and right - rear mounted light and filter unit.

Video "Light Sources for the Microscope"
http://goo.gl/IKvtDh

Base

This provides a stable support for the other parts. Bases tend to be solid to minimise distortion and ensure optical alignment, even at the highest magnification. Some bases incorporate lighting systems.

This makes most microscopes very heavy – so take care when handling and carrying.

Inverted microscopes

The conventional way to view a sample is from above. With biological material, where samples may be in liquid and/or alive, it is sometimes useful to look at the sample in a transparent container from below. Inverted microscopes are easily recognised because the objectives are underneath the stage and the lighting system is from above (figure 16).

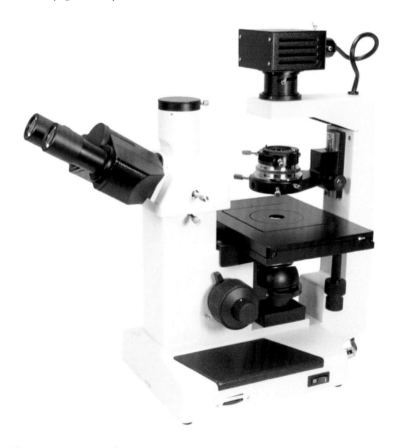

Figure 16. Inverted microscope. Light passes from the lamp above, through the condenser onto the sample. The objectives are under the stage (photo Brunel Microscopes).

Folded or portable microscopes

More portable microscopes have been designed for work in the field. In order to make them more compact, mirrors or prisms are used to wrap the light path between the objective and the eyepiece into a smaller space. The McArthur microscope is one example, and was used in early Antarctic expeditions and by the Open University in the 1970s (figure 17).

Figure 17. "McArthur" microscope formerly used by The Open University.

Specialist microscopes

This booklet is concerned with the conventional light microscope as found in most laboratories, schools, hospitals and used by amateur microscopists.

In research or in industry, microscopes can be made or adapted to a specific purpose. This may include novel illumination methods such as UV fluorescent lighting or lasers, as in confocal microscopy. These are beyond the scope of this booklet.

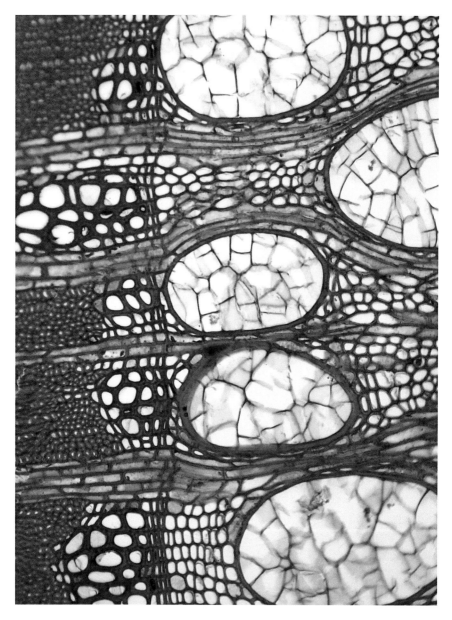

Figure 18. Tree of heaven wood section TS 250x.

Setting up your microscope with visible light

Part 1: Low magnification using a10x objective

With most microscopes, it is easiest to start with the 10x objective. If you have a lower power objective, e.g. 3.5x or 4x, this is treated separately in Part 3.

1. Select or prepare a specimen on a 3″ x 1″ glass slide in a suitable medium and covered with a small, thin glass plate called a cover slip.

   We can make a temporary preparation without the need for special equipment; sprinkle a pinch of sand at the centre of a glass slide and cover the sand with a piece of 'Sellotape'.

Figure 19. Microscope slides including a temporary one made with salt and 'Sellotape'.

2. Place your microscope on a steady table or bench.

3. Arrange seating so that you can comfortably look through the eyepiece(s).

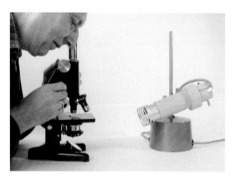 

Figure 20. Viewing position with two different microscopes.

4. Turn on the inbuilt lamp. Where you have a mirror turn it to reflect the light from an external source up into the condenser and stage (see figure 20 above). **DANGER TO EYES: DO NOT USE DIRECT SUNLIGHT. DO NOT USE A UV LAMP WITHOUT SAFETY FILTERS.**

5. Making sure that the objective will not touch the sample, place the low power 10x objective in position above the specimen (figure 21). Many microscopes have a set of objectives mounted on a revolving nosepiece. Simply move the objectives round until the one needed clicks into place.

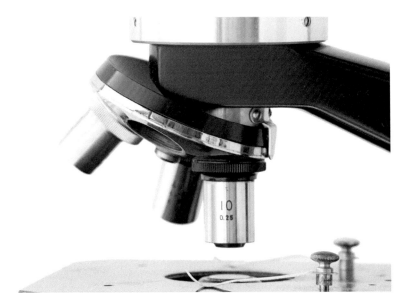

Figure 21. 10x objective rotated into place.

6. Look through the eyepiece to check that you can see a circular patch of light – there may be no sign of the specimen! If you have a binocular instrument, move the eyepieces together or apart (as you might with binoculars) to suit the distance between your eyes. If you cannot see any light, or do not see a full disk, check for obstructions in the light path.

  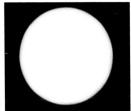

Figure 22. From left to right - Eyepiece view of light off, light turned on and then view through eyepiece showing illuminated disc.

7. Place your mounted specimen so that it is directly over the hole in the centre of the stage (figure 23).

Figure 23. Sample in place on stage of different microscopes.

8. Now, look FROM THE SIDE of the microscope and use the coarse focusing wheel to get the objective lens to within 2mm above the specimen but without touching it (figure 24).

Figure 24. Objective brought closer to sample, leaving a small gap as seen with two different microscopes.

9. Look through the eyepiece(s) and slowly **increase** the distance between the objective and specimen until you can see a clear image of your sample. Use the coarse focusing wheel but make

sure you know which way to turn it before starting this adjustment. "Fine tuning" is achieved by using the fine focusing wheel if you have one.

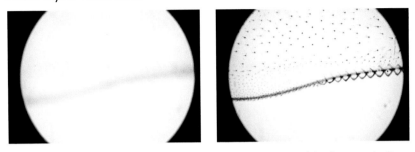

Figure 25 Initial view of a sample (Bumble bee wing) before and after focusing.

10. If the lamp has an iris diaphragm (field diaphragm): Close the diaphragm.

Figure 26. External microscope lamp showing field diaphragm open and closed.

If the condenser can be moved up and down, adjust it until the lamp iris is in focus with your sample and is in the centre of your field of view. You should have a small bright spot of light with sharp edges. Then open the iris until it just exceeds the circle seen through the eyepiece.

Figure 27. View through eyepiece, from left to right - field diaphragm closed, condenser focused to show clear small aperture, field diaphragm opened partially, diaphragm opened until just wider than circle seen through eyepiece.

If there is no lamp iris diaphragm (field diaphragm), substitute a piece of card with a pinhole in the centre and place immediately in front of the light source. Then focus the pinhole using the condenser.

Some condensers can be centred using additional adjustment knobs, so that the bright spot is central to your view. Check your microscope manual.

11. If the condenser has an adjustable iris diaphragm (aperture diaphragm):

Method 1: Remove the eyepiece and look down the tube at the back of the objective. Close the condenser iris (aperture diaphragm) until the edge appears just inside the field of view at the back of the objective. Then replace the eyepiece.

Method 2: Look through the eyepiece. Close the iris (light disk seen gets dimmer) then open gently until the point at which light does not seem to get brighter. Now close the iris a very small amount.

You need to do this every time you change the objective.

Figure 28. levers controlling the aperture diaphragm on two different microscopes.

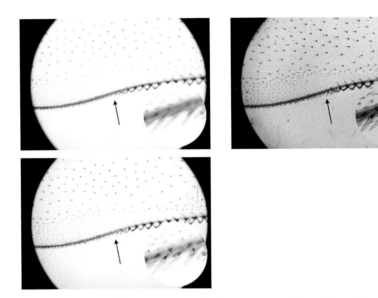

Figure 29. Top left - aperture diaphragm too wide, glare obscures image (looks soft, see inset); top right - aperture diaphragm too small, image has colour fringes and resolution is poor; bottom left - correct aperture diaphragm setting for this lens, image is in focus with best resolution.

Video Setting up your microscope
http://goo.gl/POe4Ry

Part 2. Viewing the same sample at a higher magnification, up to 40x objective

For objectives greater than 40x see Part 4.

12. Where the microscope has parfocal lenses (lenses designed as part of a matched set): Carefully rotate the next highest objective into position above the sample.

- Use the fine focus to gain a sharp image.

- Follow steps 10 to 11 in Part 1.

Where the lenses are not matched or if in doubt:

- Raise the x10 objective away from the specimen, using the coarse focus wheel.

- Follow steps 8 to 11 in Part 1 with the higher magnification objective. At stage 8, you will need to move the objective closer to the specimen without it touching.

NOTE: As you progress to higher magnifications, the depth or thickness of the subject in focus decreases. Where you might see a whole cell in focus with a 10x objective, you will find that with a 40x objective, you see different depths of the cell in focus as you adjust the fine focus wheel.

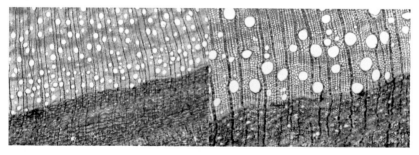

Figure 30. Eucalyptus wood TS: using 4x and a 10x objective.

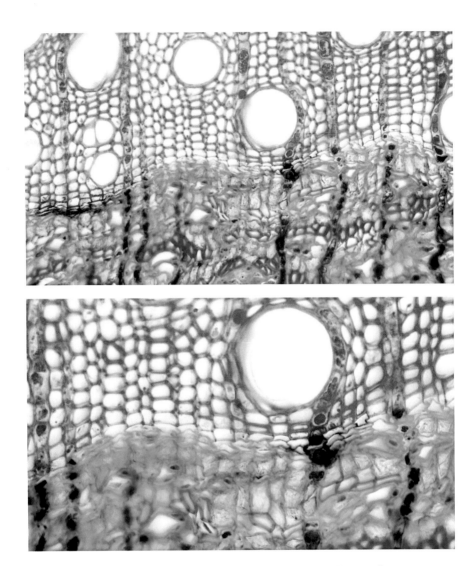

Figure 31. Eucalyptus wood TS: using 25x and 40x objectives.

Video "Using a Higher Power Objective"
http://goo.gl/Kxop1w

Part 3. Low magnification with 4x objectives or less

Many microscopes also have a low power objective, 4x or 3.5x, to gain an overview of a sample before going on to higher magnification. You may encounter one of two different scenarios. See text below and figure 32:

A. Well illuminated, full field of view. In this instance, follow the steps as in Part 1.

   Note that at step 9, "raising the objective away from the sample until the image comes into focus", you may have to raise it higher than initially expected.

B. Only the central part of the sample is illuminated, opening the field diaphragm (if present) to maximum does not help.

   Check your microscope manual. You will need to adjust your condenser. This can either involve flipping a lens on the condenser, moving an additional lens under the condenser or even changing a condenser lens (see figure 33).

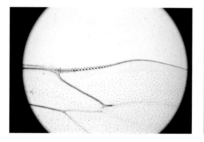 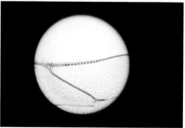

Figure 32. Two different scenarios encountered with low power 4x objectives: Left - full field of view through microscope - no action required. Right - unable to fill field of view with light – condenser may need adjusting.

Figure 33. Adaptable condensers for low power objectives. Top left - condenser with exchangeable top lens; top right - flip condenser where top lens is moved to side; Bottom row - another flip condenser showing standard setting (left) and setting for low power objective.

Check the microscope manual for your microscope to find the best settings for your low power objective (e.g. 4x) and condenser combinations.

Then follow steps 1 to 9 as in Part 1.

When you wish to go to the next highest magnification (typically a 10x objective), return the condenser settings to those you had originally (i.e. before adapting condenser for the low power 4x objective).

Then proceed as in Part 1.

Part 4. High magnification with objectives greater than 40x

The vast majority of light microscopy uses objectives over the range of 4×to 40×, which give total magnifications ranging from 20× to 500x with appropriate eyepieces.

These objectives work in air (there is an air gap between the microscope slide and the objective). Under these conditions, the maximum attainable numerical aperture is NA 1.0. This limits the maximum resolution that can be attained.

If your higher power objective has an NA greater than 1, it will be a "wet" objective, requiring a liquid bridge between the slide and the objective.

Look out for objectives labelled WI (water immersion), OI or Oel (oil immersion) and follow the manufacturer's recommendations.

The most familiar objective found on the microscope for work at high magnification is the 100x oil immersion objective. This has an NA of 1.3 or more.

To use the 100x oil immersion objective to full effect, you also need to have:

- The corresponding condenser, with an equivalent or greater numerical aperture.

- A bridge of special immersion oil between the top lens of the condenser and the underside of your microscope slide.

- A bridge of the same immersion oil between the top cover slip of your microscope slide and the 100x oil immersion objective. Note that in some instances the immersion oil is applied directly to dried uncovered smears, e.g. as in blood smears and bacteriology work.

This setup ensures that the broadest cone of light enters the condenser, passes through the sample and into the objective.

Procedure:

- Do your oil immersion work on samples after working at lower magnifications.
- Carefully place a drop of immersion oil onto the top lens of the condenser with a numerical aperture of 1.3 or greater.
- Lower the condenser.
- Place the sample slide on the stage.
- Raise the condenser until an oil bridge is created between the condenser and the underside of the slide.
- Use your 40x objective to focus on the sample.
- Focus the condenser and adjust the field iris diaphragm and aperture iris diaphragm.
- Find the subject you want to view with the oil immersion objective.
- Swing the 40x objective away from the sample and place a drop of immersion oil on the top of the slide/cover slip.
- If your oil immersion objective is parfocal with your 40 times objective, carefully swing it into position above the sample. The oil bridge between sample slide and oil immersion objective should be established.
- If you do not know whether your oil immersion objective is parfocal, lower the stage slightly (or raise the objectives) before swinging the oil immersion objective into place. Then looking from the side, bring the oil immersion objective in contact with the oil drop on the slide. The distance required between the objective lens and your cover slip will be too small to see. Therefore carefully use the fine focus whilst looking through the microscope to lower the objective until

the sample is in focus. Many high power oil immersion objectives have a sprung front lens to reduce the likelihood of damage to lens and sample in case of impact.

- Use the fine focus to get your subject into sharp view.

- Adjust your aperture diaphragm.

- View the sample.

- At this magnification a mechanical stage is indispensable for small controlled lateral movements if you need to scan the slide.

- You may need to repeat the entire procedure for every slide.

- When you have finished using the oil immersion objective, carefully clean the objective and the condenser of oil using lens tissues.

- Clean your slides of oil or discard safely.

After completing your session on the microscope

13. When finished:2

- Turn off microscope light;

- Set back to lowest power objective;

- Protect microscope from dust until next use.

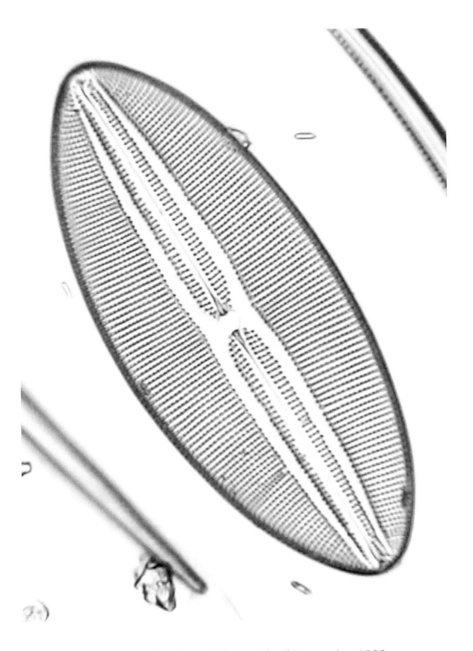

Figure 34. Diatom, Diploneis sp. Taken with oil immersion 1000x.

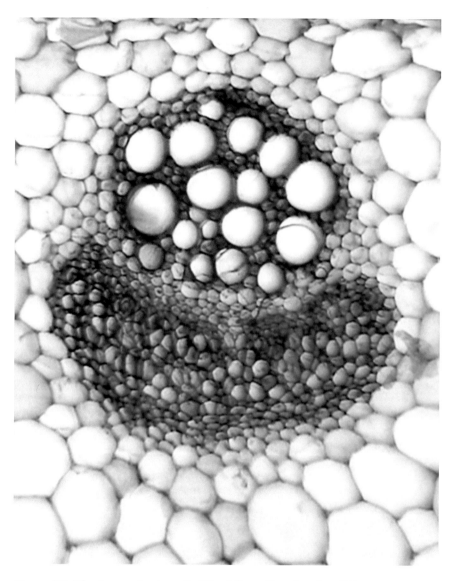

Figure 35. Plant vascular bundle TS, oblique illumination 250x.

Nine Points of Microscope Care

A well-constructed microscope can last a lifetime, if cared for properly.

1. Train yourself and anyone else using your microscope(s) in the correct use of the instrument.

2. When not in use, store your microscope in a dust free environment, preferably in its box or hood or under a microscope cover.

3. Store in a dry environment, avoiding temperature extremes.

4. Take care when moving a microscope, they are generally heavy. If you have to lift or carry one, hold by the microscope arm (see figure 3) and under the base.

5. Keep your condenser, objectives and eyepieces clean. They are valuable, high precision optical components. First, use a soft brush to remove dust. Then <u>gently</u> use a damp lens cloth or lens cleaning tissue to clean accessible glass surfaces if necessary. Other materials or solvents may damage the lenses or any coatings on them.

6. Avoid damaging objectives. This can occur if you lower high power objectives so that they crash into your sample slide. When in storage, ensure the objectives are clear of the stage and that they will not be damaged by other objects impacting on them.

7. Light sources have a limited lifetime. Turn off the microscope light once you have finished working with the instrument.

8. Store microscope manuals and tools at a known location close to the microscope for easy access.

9. Conduct an annual maintenance check on your microscope. If there are issues, get the microscope professionally cleaned and serviced.

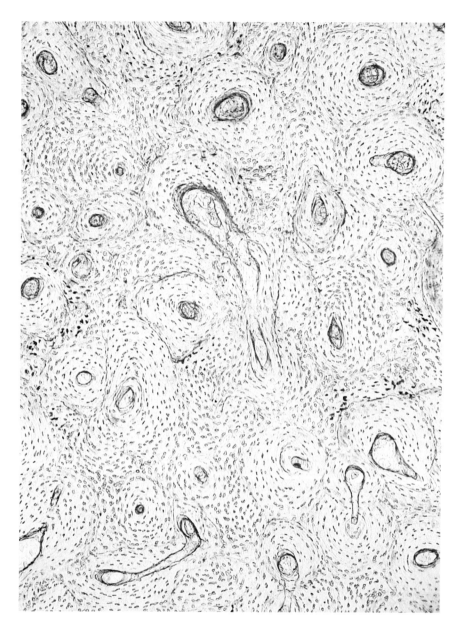

Figure36. Bone TS 100x.

Troubleshooting

Light too bright:

- *Adjust lamp brightness if possible.*
- *Alternatively use neutral density filters between light and condenser.*
- *If using light with microscope mirror, move light further away and check that using flat mirror, not a concave one (unless there is no condenser on your instrument).*

Light too dim:

- *Check light plugged in.*
- *Check light bulb is working.*
- *Adjust lamp brightness if possible.*
- *Check that there are no filters between light and condenser.*
- *Check that condenser diaphragm (aperture diaphragm) is set correctly.*
- *If using mirror and lamp, ensure that the mirror is angled correctly to reflect light into the condenser. Move lamp closer.*
- *If in a very bright room, turn down lights or even work in a darkroom.*

Visible disk of light too small

- *Open lamp iris diaphragm (field diaphragm).*
- *If you are using an objective of less than 10x magnification. Your condenser may either have a supplementary lens just for this instance, or the facility to move the top lens of the condenser out of the light path to give a broader illuminated area. This will give a poorer resolution if used with higher magnification objectives.*

No image visible:

- *Your sample may be too opaque.*
- *Check that the specimen is in the correct position.*
- *Check that your objective lens is 'clicked' (or screwed) into position properly.*
- *Repeat the above steps 8 to 11.*
- *Check that the light is properly arranged.*
- *Another possibility is that you have turned the coarse focusing wheel too quickly and moved past the point of focus without spotting it. Repeat steps 8 to 11 in Part 1.*
- *Try using an easy test specimen such as gauze with a 10x objective.*

Double vision with microscopes with two eyepieces:

- *Adjust the separation between the two eyepieces to suit your vision.*
- *Alternatively, place a piece of black card over one eyepiece and just view the sample through one eyepiece.*
- *If your microscope has interchangeable binocular and monocular heads, switch over to the monocular one.*

Not seeing the expected sample, artefacts:

- *Particularly with pale or sparse samples, you can accidently focus either on the top of the cover slip, the underside of the slide or even the condenser lens. Repeat steps 8 to 11 in Part 1 again and move the focus more slowly.*
- *Air bubbles may be included in slides or you may find your slide drying out. Figure 37 is a particularly dramatic example. Check your slide visually and try another, unaffected area.*

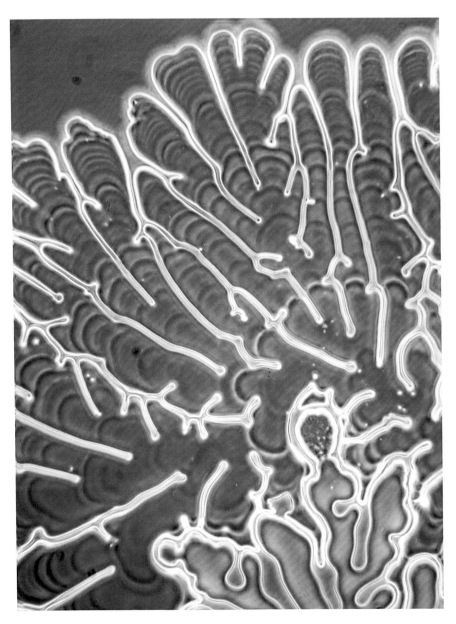

Figure 37. Artefacts created by drying out glycerine gel (under phase contrast) 250x.

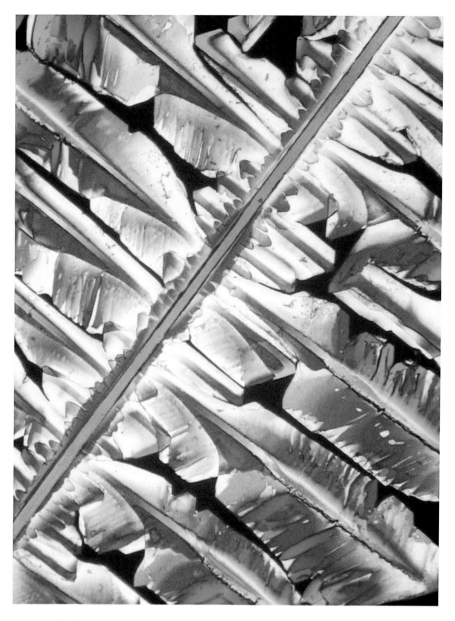

Figure 38. Paracetamol & codeine crystals using polarisation filters.

Next steps

This booklet lets you use the compound light microscope for many applications; as a tool in the workplace, the laboratory or in your home.

Once you are comfortable with using a compound light microscope, you are likely to start raising further questions, for example:

1. How do I record what I see through the microscope?

2. How can I increase the contrast/visibility of my subjects under the microscope?

3. How can I use the microscope to the maximum of its capabilities?

Further booklets in this microscopy series will cover subjects including:

- Photography through the microscope;

- Light & contrast methods for the compound microscope;

- Lenses, images and resolution in the compound microscope.

Your opinion counts

We hope that you have found this booklet useful. If you have any comments, insights or simply microscopy experiences you would like to share, please do get in touch by e-mailing me, Chris Thomas, at chris@miltoncontact.com.

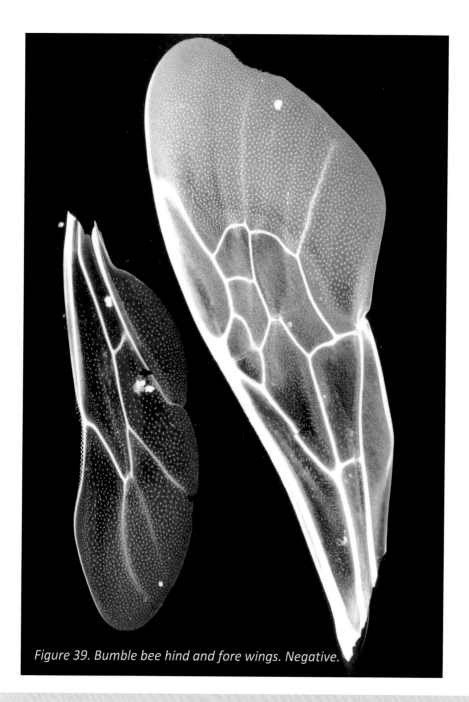

Figure 39. Bumble bee hind and fore wings. Negative.

About the Authors

Dr Chris Thomas

I have had a microscope or three for most of my life! I've used them for pleasure and professionally when I worked as a research scientist in commercial plant molecular biology for over 20 years.

I need to know how things work. This helps me with my current interest of photographing through the microscope for pleasure.

Lewis and I teamed up again because we wanted to provide a no-nonsense, straightforward guide on using the compound microscope, following on from our previous successful collaboration on "Understanding and using the Stereomicroscope".

Lewis Woolnough

I'm a retired headteacher and have pursued microscopy with a passion for the past 20 years. I also use my microscopes as a beekeeper and now regularly give courses in microscopy to others.

My previous book "Understanding and using the Stereomicroscope", designed and published with Chris's help, was a great success.

Like Chris, I believe in providing guidance and information in an accessible way. This book is for those who need or want to use compound microscopes either professionally, as interested amateurs or as absolute beginners.

We are both members of microscopy organisations such as the Quekett Microscopical Club and the Postal Microscopy Society. Lewis is also a member of the Royal Microscopical Society.

Figure 40. Mammoth fine hair, photographed between crossed polarisation filters 100x.

Acknowledgements

Putting this booklet together has been a mammoth task. Our thanks go to Pam Hamer who acted as a critical friend.

Brunel Microscopes provided photographs of currently available microscope models.

Louise Thomas, our glamorous microscopy video star.

Our families, who put up with our spending time on this book.

And above all, our fellow microscopists who have shared their interests and experiences over the decades. Our knowledge is built on their shoulders.

Whilst we are indebted to all who helped us with this project, any deficiencies and errors in the content rest solely with us.

Other Useful Resources

- Royal Microscopical Society http://www.rms.org.uk/
- Quekett Microscopical Club http://www.quekett.org/
- Postal Microscopical Society http://www.postal-microscopical-society.org.uk/
- Micscape http://www.microscopy-uk.org.uk/index.html
- Brunel Microscopes http://www.brunelmicroscopes.co.uk/
- **Our website** www.usingthemicroscope.com

(Links correct at time of publication)